MUD AND THE MASTERPIECE

SEEING YOURSELF AND OTHERS THROUGH THE EYES OF JESUS

DISCUSSION GUIDE

John Burke

Discussion Guide written by Michael D. Warden

Contents

How To Use This Discussion Guide

Thanks so much for purchasing this discussion guide for my book, *Mud and the Masterpiece.* I hope you and your small group or leadership team will find your exploration of the book as challenging and meaningful as I did in creating it. As you'll see in the book, I'm definitely passionate about the timeliness and importance of this message for Christ followers everywhere. Yet, I know I'm just one member of Christ's Body. My voice alone simply can't bring about the kind of large-scale change I truly believe Jesus longs to see happen in churches all across the country and the world. I know that whatever real change is going to happen is going to start with you. It's through small groups of devoted Christ followers just like you – people willing to take an honest look at themselves and take bold steps to follow Jesus in a more transparent, grace-filled way – that real change will come. That's why I want you to know I'm praying for you...that God will grant you grace to experience his amazing love for you and for people everywhere in a new way, and strengthen your courage to step out and love those far from Christ in the same way Jesus did.

This discussion guide includes six, 90-minute sessions, each covering a handful of chapters from the book. Each session is split into three parts: CONNECT, DISCUSS, and DO. I encourage you not to skip any of the sections, as I really believe they are all essential to helping us really learn together how to follow Jesus more authentically in our daily lives. Make sure people know to read the assigned chapters ahead of time, and really encourage one another to take on the challenges in each "DO" section and share what they learned in the "CONNECT" section at the following session.

My prayer is that this book will lead you to exhibit more of the attitudes and actions of Jesus. To help you do more than just discuss this book and then move on, we've created an Action Guide as a companion to whatever curriculum you do after *Mud and the Masterpiece*. The Action Guide only requires 10-15 minutes each group session to check in with each other on the practical actions or attitudes of Jesus you've acted on that week. You can download the Action Guide at www.MudandtheMasterpiece.com.

Finally, I'd love to hear from you! Share with us your thoughts and impressions from your exploration of *Mud and the Masterpiece*, and let us know how studying this book together has impacted your small group or leadership team. Just drop me a note on www.JohnBurkeOnline.com.

God's blessings,

John Burke

DISCUSSION GUIDE

Introduction & Chapter 1

"I'm convinced that our problem is not that we need more evangelistic tools, methods, apologetic arguments, or missional strategies—in fact, none of these will be worth anything if we don't first see ourselves and others through the eyes of Jesus. I truly believe people intuitively sense how we feel about them (even in a ten-minute conversation), and that makes the biggest difference of all."
– John Burke, *Mud and the Masterpiece*

In advance of this first session, make sure participants know to read the Introduction and Chapter 1 of *Mud and the Masterpiece* before they come.

Connect 30 MINUTES

After everyone has arrived, start the conversation by giving each person a minute or two to "check in" – that is, to share briefly with the group who they are, where they are from, how they got connected to this discussion group, and one thing they hope to get out of the experience. Don't skip this. Checking in is an easy but effective way to help people feel connected to the group, "plug in," and get fully present.

NOTE: If you have more than 12 people in your group, form groups of three or four to do your check in.

After everyone has checked in, take a moment to pray, inviting God to open your minds and hearts, to guide your conversation, and to give you courage to follow where He leads.

Before you launch into your discussion of the Introduction and Chapter 1, it's a good idea to lay a few ground rules together about what you do or don't want to be part of your overall experience together as you go through the book. Here are a few foundational group agreements that can really help your exploration together be as powerful and life-giving as it can be.

Shared Agreements

1. **No perfect people allowed!**
   We give each other full permission to not be perfect or "have it all together."
   We welcome the authentic in one another, and understand we're all on a journey of becoming the people God wants us to be.

2. **No Fixing.**
   When someone shares a question they're wrestling with, or some other struggle they're having, we won't try to "fix" them by diagnosing what we think is wrong with them, or tell them what to do. Rather, we will ask open-ended questions, and only offer advice when it is requested.

3. **Come as you are, but don't stay that way.**
   Though we fully accept one another just as we are (see Agreement #1!), we are here to grow together, and will actively encourage each other to step out of our comfort zones, stretch and grow as we explore how to follow Jesus better.

Feel free to add any other agreements your group wants to include. Make sure each person feels comfortable with each agreement before moving on to the next. When you're finished, type up all the agreements and keep a copy on hand every time you meet.

Discuss **40 MINUTES**

Begin by asking:
- What was your reaction to what you read in the Introduction and Chapter 1?
- What stood out to you?
- What surprised or intrigued you?
- What did you find confusing or even frustrating?
- What did you learn or discover?

 Have someone read aloud this quote from Chapter 1, page 22:

"Maybe the reason people today are drawn to Jesus, but not his followers, is because many Christians are NOT like Jesus—we don't really see what Jesus sees in other people. We don't really feel the way Jesus felt toward people straying far from God, living messy lives. Christians can subtly become pharisaical without even realizing it!"

Discuss:
- What do you think – do you agree with Burke's assertion? Why or why not?
- If you agree...how do you suppose this happens? How do people who sincerely want to follow Jesus end up becoming pharisaical without even realizing it?

Burke challenges us to wrestle with this question throughout the book: "Am I more like Jesus or more like a Pharisee to the people around me?" (page 22). Let's take a moment to have each person share their own answer to that question, as honestly and straightforwardly as they can. We'll check in again at the end of our book study to see what, if anything, has shifted in our understanding of ourselves and our impact on those who are far from Christ.

 Have someone read aloud this story from the book, pages 22-23:

"When my wife and I lived in St. Petersburg, Russia, I got to see one of my favorite paintings housed in the Hermitage Museum. It's Rembrandt's famous painting Return of the Prodigal Son. It depicts that moving scene in Jesus' parable when, 'filled with compassion' (Luke 15:20), the father (God) ran toward his wayward son. The son had squandered his inheritance with loose living, but came begging for mercy. The father embraced him, saying, 'My son was dead but now is alive, was lost but now he's found' (see Luke 15:24). Jesus paints this beautiful, priceless picture in answer to the religious people's complaint that he 'welcomes sinners' (Luke 15:2). The painting is worth a fortune.

"Now just imagine if one day you visit St. Petersburg and there, in a back-alley dumpster, you discover Rembrandt's masterpiece, but it's hardly recognizable. It's covered in mud and dirt, it's stained, and the canvas has been torn. You wouldn't recognize it at all except you notice the famous hand of the father on the ragged son's back.

"How would you treat this painting? Would you treat it like trash? It's covered in mud, stained and torn—is it worthless? Do you treat it like it's worthless? Or would you treat it like a million-dollar masterpiece that needs to be handled with care and restored? I'm guessing all of us could see past the mud and even the damage to recognize the immense value inherent in this one-of-a-kind work of art—simply because it was created by Rembrandt's own hand. We wouldn't try to clean it up ourselves; we would bring it to a master, who could delicately restore it to its original condition.

"So why do we struggle to treat people like the immensely valuable, one-of-a-kind Masterpiece God created with his own hand? As I study the life and interactions of Jesus with very sin-stained, muddied people, it becomes evident that Jesus could see something worth dying for in all the people he encountered. Jesus could see past the mud to the Masterpiece God wanted to restore."

Discuss:

- What do you tend to see most when you look in the mirror – the mud, or the Masterpiece God wants to restore?
- Why do you suppose that is?
- Burke asserts, "What you focus on determines who you become and the impact you have on people around you." How might your experience of life be different if you focused more on the Masterpiece than the mud – both in yourself, and in others?
- What's stopping you from living this way?
- What do you think it would really take to make the change?

 Have someone read this quote from Chapter 1, page 31:

"Is it possible that many Christians today who desire moral reform, love the Word of God, and pride themselves on teaching truth could be missional on the wrong mission—failing to demonstrate the heart of God to a broken world?

"Absolutely!

"Hey, if Jesus called Peter 'the rock,' and yet Peter was deceived at least twice, if James and John missed Jesus' heart several times, if Paul was zealous for God yet persecuted the church... who do I think I am if I proudly say, 'Not me!' Phariseeism can sneak up on all of us!

"So what was it that caused the Pharisees to be zealous for the wrong mission?

"They had no mercy or compassion for broken, muddied people! They did many things right, but they didn't see themselves or others accurately. They had an 'us/them' mentality. They believed God belonged to the 'good people' (us) and wanted nothing to do with the 'bad people' (them). So they separated themselves. That's where Jesus and the Pharisees collided."

Discuss:

- How do Christ followers – even well-meaning Christ followers – perpetuate this same "us/them" mentality in our culture today?
- What about you? When have you caught yourself falling into an "us/them," "good people/ bad people" mentality about others? Why do you suppose you started thinking that way?
- If, as Burke asserts, Phariseeism is a perpetual danger for all those who follow Jesus, how do we avoid it?

Do 20 MINUTES

As the discussion draws to a close, go around the room and have each person respond to these questions:

- What are you taking away from our time together today? What do you most want to remember from our conversation?
- What action has our discussion inspired you to take in your own life? Will you do it?

 Finally, here's a challenge for the entire group to take on together (from the book, page 36):

"Ask God to lead you to people this week who look muddied to you. Engage them in conversation. Your only goal is to ask questions, listen, and learn about them as people, uniquely created by the Master Artist."

Ask each person:

- Will you take on that challenge?

We'll check in on how your challenge went the next time we meet. Also, remind everyone to read Chapters 2 and 3 before our next meeting!

Close with prayer, and dismiss.

DISCUSSION GUIDE

Chapters 2 & 3

"Be kind, for everyone you meet is fighting a great battle."
– Plato

Connect 30 MINUTES

After everyone has arrived, start the conversation by giving each person a minute or two to "check in" around the following questions:

- How'd it go with your assignment? What happened?
- What did you learn?
- How do you want to apply what you've learned moving forward?

Don't rush through this part. Aside from helping each other "get fully connected here," checking in on what happened with the previous assignment is a terrific way to learn from one another's challenges and experiences.

NOTE: If you have more than 12 people in your group, form groups of three or four to do your check in.

After everyone has checked in, remind everyone of your shared agreements. Then take a moment to pray, inviting God to open your minds and hearts, to guide your conversation, and to give you courage to follow where He leads.

Discuss 40 MINUTES

Begin by asking:

- What was your reaction to what you read in Chapters 2 and 3?
- What stood out to you?
- What surprised or intrigued you?
- What did you find confusing or even frustrating?
- What did you learn or discover?

Then continue by discussing:

- In Chapter 2, Burke talks about the need for Christ followers to be "unshockable" in their interactions with people far from Christ. What do you think he means by that?
- On a scale of 1 to 10 (10 being "Nothing shocks me. Ever."), how unshockable do you think you are around people who are far from Christ?

Let's try this quick survey. Slowly read aloud the list below of different kinds of people. As you do, have group members raise their hand for each "kind of person" they might feel uneasy or uncomfortable striking up a conversation with:

a drug addict
a conservative
a Buddhist
a convicted felon
a convicted molester
someone of a different culture or ethnicity
a "beautiful" person
a lesbian
a Muslim
a vocal Christian
a Wiccan
a vocal atheist
a "successful person"
a person in a wheelchair
a liberal
a Hindu
a gay couple
a stripper
a troubled person

After the survey, discuss:

- Why do you suppose Christ followers sometimes feel uneasy engaging with people like these?
- Why do we label people like this?
- How might using labels like these undermine our ability to see the Masterpiece in others?

 Have someone read aloud this quote from Chapter 2, pages 44-45:

"Our view of 'what kind' of people we are changes our behavior. The Pharisees identified the immoral woman by her mud. 'If [Jesus] were a prophet, he would know...what kind of woman she is' (Luke 7:39, italics mine). What kind of a woman is she? They could only see the mud, so they treated her like dirt. Jesus saw what kind of woman she was created to be!

"It's an identity issue. Do you see the image of God in every person? Can you imagine God's original intention for one life? That must have been what Jesus could see! He somehow helped people identify 'what kind' of people God created them to be. The Pharisees did not have the spiritual vision to see what kind of woman she was created to be, so they inadvertently did the work of the destroyer, who keeps people enslaved to their sin by keeping them identified with sin. What kind of people are we? That's a critical question. How do we see ourselves and others?"

Discuss:

- What does it mean to identify a person with the Masterpiece God created them to be rather than the mud on their canvas?
- What does that look like in real life? How would you know whether you were doing one or the other – what signs would you look for?
- What do you think makes engaging the "Masterpiece first" in people so difficult for many Christ followers?
- What makes it difficult for you?

 Have someone read aloud this quote from Chapter 3, pages 60-61:

"Are we more like Jesus or the Pharisees? It's not so obvious. I find that pharisaical judgmentalism grows weeds in my garden of good deeds, and I'm blind to it. For a whole week, I tried to be more conscious of what I hold in my mind's eye about people.

Here's what I discovered:

"Judging is fun!"

"Judging others makes you feel good, and I'm not sure I've gone a single day without this sin. In any given week, I might condemn my son numerous times for a messy room; judge my daughter for being moody—which especially bothers me when I'm being moody (but I have a good reason!). I judge my wife for over-involvement in service (because it raises the bar for me); even my dog gets the hammer of condemnation for his bad breath (though we feed him junk but don't brush his teeth). Some of you may be thinking, 'Wait, are you saying that correcting my kids for a messy room is judging?' NO! But there's correction that values with mercy and there's correction that devalues with judgment."

"I watch the news and condemn those 'idiotic people' who do such things. Most reality TV shows are full of people I can judge as sinful, ignorant, stupid, arrogant, or childish. I get in my car and drive and find a host of inept drivers who should have flunked their driving test—and I throw in a little condemnation on our Department of Public Safety for good measure!"

"At the store, I complain to myself about the brainless lack of organization that makes it impossible to find what I'm looking for, all the while being tortured with Muzak—who picks that music anyway? I stand in the shortest line, which I judge is way too long because—'LOOK PEOPLE—it says "10 items or less," and I count more than that in three of your baskets—what's wrong with you people?' And why can't that teenage checker—what IS she wearing—focus and work so we can get out of here?"

"Judging is our favorite pastime, if we're honest—but we're not! We're great at judging the world around us by standards we would highly resent being held to! Judging makes us feel good because it puts us in a better light than others—we put ourselves in the place of God, the standard bearer! Jesus confronted this God complex in those who judged by their own standards, but didn't judge themselves by God's standards of mercy, justice, and faithfulness (Matthew 23:23)."

Discuss:

- What's so seductive about judging others?
- How does judging others actually blind us from seeing them through God's eyes?
- What do you think has to happen in a person's heart and mind for him or her to stop judging and genuinely begin to see others as God's Masterpiece?

 Have someone read aloud this quote from Chapter 3, page 55:

"People perceive how you feel about them, intuitively, and that's what they respond to. Training in what to say, arguments that prove you're right, tracts or pamphlets, and good books can either help or hinder depending on one thing: what's in your heart toward that person. That's what matters most! That's what influences people the most, even if they can't consciously articulate why.

"Which means, if we are going to be influential people—life-giving people, people who are more like Jesus—we must pay attention to the mental frameworks we put people in. The picture we hold of them in our hearts, the way we feel about them more than the words we say, techniques we use, or truth we proclaim—these have the greatest impact.

"If you are truly for people, if you hold good will toward them in your heart, if you highly value them, people can hear all kinds of difficult things because they'll know you are on their side. But if what you hold in your heart toward another person is devaluing, judging, condescending, manipulative, or self-centered, people sniff that out like dogs in the dog park."

Discuss:

- What do you want people who are far from Christ to say about their interactions with you?
- What would you hate for them to say about their encounters with you?
- What kind of person would you have to be to have the impact you want?
- For you to become that kind of person, what do you need to let go of?
- What do you need to learn to do better?
- What new risks do you need to take?

Do 20 MINUTES

As the discussion draws to a close, go around the room and have each person respond to these questions:

- What are you taking away from our time together today? What do you most want to remember from our conversation?
- What action has our discussion inspired you to take in your own life? Will you do it?

 Finally, here's a challenge for the entire group to take on together (from the book, page 70):

"Tomorrow and the next day, wake up saying, 'Lord, show me your assignment for me today. I'm available.' With each person you encounter, ask, 'Lord, what do you want me to see? How can I encourage or restore value to this person?' See it and say it."

Ask each person:

- Will you take on that challenge?

We'll check in on how your challenge went the next time we meet. Also, remind everyone to read Chapters 4 through 6 before our next meeting!

Close with prayer, and dismiss.

DISCUSSION GUIDE

Chapters 4 through 6

"It is a serious thing to live in a society of possible gods and goddesses, to remember that the dullest and most uninteresting person you talk to may one day be a creature which, if you saw it now, you would be strongly tempted to worship, or else a horror and a corruption such as you now meet, if at all, only in a nightmare. All day long we are, in some degree, helping each other to one or other of these destinations. It is in the light of these overwhelming possibilities...that we should conduct all our dealings with one another, all friendships, all loves, all play, all politics. There are no "ordinary" people. You have never talked to a mere mortal."
– C.S. Lewis

Connect 30 MINUTES

After everyone has arrived, start the conversation by giving each person a minute or two to "check in" around the following questions:

- How'd it go with your assignment? What happened?
- What did you learn?
- How do you want to apply what you've learned moving forward?

Don't rush through this part. Aside from helping each other "get fully connected here," checking in on what happened with the previous assignment is a terrific way to learn from one another's challenges and experiences.

NOTE: If you have more than 12 people in your group, form groups of three or four to do your check in.

After everyone has checked in, remind everyone of your shared agreements. Then take a moment to pray, inviting God to open your minds and hearts, to guide your conversation, and to give you courage to follow where He leads.

Discuss 40 MINUTES

Begin by asking:

- What was your reaction to what you read in Chapters 4-6?
- What stood out to you?
- What surprised or intrigued you?
- What did you find confusing or even frustrating?
- What did you learn or discover?

 Have someone read aloud this story from Chapter 4, pages 78-79:

"Scottie was born with spina bifida. The doctors told Sarah, his mother, to unplug life support. The baby wouldn't survive a year. Sarah refused, and Scottie survived the first year, then the second...then the tenth...and twentieth! But life wasn't easy for Sarah. She had seven sons (two who died tragically). In his twenties, Scottie had his legs amputated and was wheelchair-bound. The father abandoned the family, leaving them destitute and forcing Sarah to move into low-income housing. Without a wheelchair ramp, for fifteen years Scottie found himself confined to their apartment while Sarah worked.

"The new manager of Scottie's apartment noticed Scottie. She had just started following Christ and was learning how God's Spirit prompts us to value those the world discards. Nudged, she took the risk to invite Sarah and Scottie to church one Sunday. Sarah declined because they didn't have the right clothes. The manager assured her our church was 'come as you are.' They did, and Sarah and Scottie kept coming.

One Sunday, Bill Aguayo passed by Scottie and reacted in disgust. Thinking Oh, he's just a nub of a man, misshaped head bent to the side, no legs, he steered clear to avoid the awkward feelings that erupted. Bill recalls, 'All day, God wouldn't leave me alone. I kept thinking about the value God placed on this deformed man who repulsed me, and I knew God wanted me to go meet him.'"

Discuss:

- When have you felt like a "Scottie?" In what way are we all "Scotties?"
- When have you felt like Bill? What happened?
- Seems we've all got a little bit of Scottie and little bit of Bill in us. Given that, do you think we can really be like Jesus, seeing the Masterpiece through the most leprous, untouchable person, and point out their value to God? If so, how?
- In Chapter 4 (pages 80-88), Burke asserts that all people are created in God's image and can reflect that image in their lives – particularly through their ability to create, manage (or govern), and love. Given this, what are some specific ways we can call out God's Masterpiece in others around us?

 Have someone read aloud "The Value of Turkish Violas" from Chapter 5, pages 99-101:

"Dervish was heartbroken. He had followed the love of his life around the world, from Turkey to Austin. But now she had broken his heart, and his two years in Austin felt wasted. Why did he give up touring Europe with a world-renowned orchestra for a woman? He felt like throwing his expensive Turkish viola across the room, but it was too valuable to waste on a flash of fury.

Love had lured him to Austin. He just didn't realize whose love. Distraught, not knowing what do to with himself, Dervish went to Dominican Joe, his favorite coffee shop in Austin. Sitting outside next to a group of people laughing and talking, Dervish noticed Phillip, who seemed to be leading this group in some kind of discussion. Eavesdropping, he overheard talk about life and meaning.

Dervish felt drawn to them. He asked what they were discussing. Phillip encouraged Dervish to join their quote study. Little did Dervish know, but he had just been led to a Gateway Network composed of musicians, filmmakers, and artists. Their quote study, based on wisdom from the book of James and other recognizable quotes from authors or artists, was a way the group engaged people in spiritual conversation after they played a set of music in local venues. That night Phillip invited Dervish to a birthday bash at his house.

Later that week at Phillip's party, Dervish met Ramy (our Egyptian pastor to artists). Dervish had never experienced such an authentic combination of laughter and honesty about real life struggles. Sitting around the fire pit that night with Ramy and others, Dervish opened up about his own broken heart. From this group of strangers, he felt genuine care and concern. There was a love that wasn't verbalized, but it was palpable to Dervish.

'Dude, you need to come hang out with us more!' Ramy said before they parted ways. 'You know, sometimes you follow the wrong things to the right place! Come to my house next week. This group meets regularly to help each other grow as artists, musicians, and spiritually. You'll fit in perfectly! You'll love it.'

Just feeling loved and valued by fellow artists felt comforting to Dervish. He kept coming to Network events, and even though he was Muslim, he got the clear message 'You're valuable—just come be with us and grow with us!' As Dervish learned more and more about these 'Jesus people' and what they believed, he became more open. They listened to his religious views with respect, focusing on God rather than religion, and he felt loved and valued and wanted regardless.

Dervish joined one of Ramy's small groups that was reading and studying the Bible. He also decided to read the whole Qur'an, something he had not done. Ramy invited Dervish to play viola with the band, sometimes at gigs, sometimes for worship at church. The love and value his heart experienced kept him openly seeking to understand the God of the Bible.

"Two years later, I felt prompted one night to ask a question. 'Dervish, you've been hanging out with us a few years; where are you with Jesus?' What he said showed amazing insight.

'You know, I've read the entire Bible and the whole Qur'an, and they say almost the same things about right and wrong. There's one difference: Grace!'

'Wow, Dervish, that's incredibly insightful,' I told him. Then I decided to point out his value to this God of grace. 'Dervish, do you realize how much the God of grace loves you? Think about it, he guided you around the world so that you could know and experience his great love. Do you realize that?'

'Yes, I do. It's amazing.' Dervish shook his head as if struck by the gravity of it.

'I mean, what are the odds of coming upon Ramy and that group of musicians who would welcome you in and give you the time and space to explore faith?'

'I know, I know' was all Dervish could say through a huge grin and moistening eyes.

Two months later, Dervish got baptized for his faith in Jesus, and I'm sure that God will use him as a tool of restoration for many others around the world in the years to come! But it all started because Phillip, Ramy, and other Christ-followers conveyed the message 'You're valuable enough to be with.' 'You have gifts God's given you to serve him—come join us.'"

Discuss:

- What's your reaction to this story?
- Have you ever had an experience like Phillip and Ramy did with Dervish? If so, tell us about it. What happened? What was it like for you to invite someone who didn't yet follow Christ into your life? What did you learn through the experience?
- If you've never had an experience like this, what has gotten in the way? What would have to change (either in you or your circumstances) for you to begin having experiences like this?
- On a scale of 1 to 10 (10 being "completely willing and available"), how willing are you to enter into the messiness of people's lives the way Phillip and Ramy did with Dervish? Why do you suppose that is?

 Have someone read this quote from Chapter 6, page 109:

"Most of us grew up under what Dallas Willard calls 'condemnation engineering'—it's the way of the world. If someone doesn't behave the way you would like, you subtly shame, cajole, manipulate, or condemn their very being until they work hard to conform, or else. Near and dear to the heart of the Pharisee is this system of working for something—earning and deserving, living up to the standard you control, punishment and rewards, excluding or judging those who can't live up. This makes up the life of a Pharisee, but it's also the system most of the world works under. It may produce conformity for a short while, but it doesn't change the heart of a person.

Condemnation engineering easily sneaks up on Christians. The modern-day Pharisee says to herself, 'I don't do these wrong things, I do these right things, therefore I'm good in God's eyes.' When the Pharisee looks at those who don't live up to her standards, she subtly communicates, 'Unless you get your act together and work like I have to morally approximate these standards, God wants nothing to do with you.'"

Discuss:

- In what ways have you experienced "condemnation engineering" in your life?
- Looking back, what has been the overall impact of condemnation engineering on your heart?
- When are you most tempted to try to fix, manipulate, or force change on people?
- How might this relate to the way you see yourself and others as less valuable than God sees them?
- How can we better respect the value and freedom God has given others?

Do 20 MINUTES

As the discussion draws to a close, go around the room and have each person respond to these questions:

- What are you taking away from our time together today? What do you most want to remember from our conversation?
- What action has our discussion inspired you to take in your own life? Will you do it?

Finally, here's a challenge for the entire group to take on together (from the book, page 125):

"If you've been doing these exercises, hopefully there are one or two people you've engaged in conversation. Asking respects freedom, so this week try asking them spiritual questions without telling (unless you're asked). Just keep asking questions and listening to see what God might be doing in their lives. Something as simple as, 'Tell me about your spiritual background,' can launch great conversations. Be curious without judgment and watch what God does."

Ask each person:

- Will you take on that challenge?

We'll check in on how your challenge went the next time we meet. Also, remind everyone to read Chapters 7 through 9 before our next meeting!

Close with prayer, and dismiss.

DISCUSSION GUIDE

Chapters 7 through 9

"Compassion is the sometimes fatal capacity for feeling what it's like to live inside someone else's skin. It is the knowledge that there can never really be any peace and joy for me until there is peace and joy finally for you too."
– Frederick Buechner

Connect 30 MINUTES

After everyone has arrived, start the conversation by giving each person a minute or two to "check in" around the following questions:

- How'd it go with your assignment? What happened?
- What did you learn?
- How do you want to apply what you've learned moving forward?

Don't rush through this part. Aside from helping each other "get fully here," checking in on what happened with the previous assignment is a terrific way to learn from one another's challenges and experiences.

NOTE: If you have more than 12 people in your group, form groups of three or four to do your check in.

After everyone has checked in, remind everyone of your shared agreements. Then take a moment to pray, inviting God to open your minds and hearts, to guide your conversation, and to give you courage to follow where He leads.

Discuss 40 MINUTES

Begin by asking:

- What was your reaction to what you read in Chapters 7-9?
- What stood out to you?
- What surprised or intrigued you?
- What did you find confusing or even frustrating?
- What did you learn or discover?

 Have someone read aloud this quote from Chapter 7, page 130:

"Jesus entered into people's pain, hurt, and places of deep need, and he showed them how much God cares. Picture what Jesus actually did the most: He spent morning to evening for three years meeting people at their greatest points of pain and need! It didn't matter to him if they believed in him yet or not; he started where they felt the most need. If we want to treat people the way Jesus did, we must do the same."

Discuss:

- What might it look like for Christ followers to "do the same" – that is, meet people at their point of need regardless of whether they believe in Jesus yet?
- If you lived your life this way more intentionally, what would be different?
- What's the cost of doing life this way? What's the pay off? Is it worth it?

 Have someone read aloud Matthew 9:35-36, then this quote from Chapter 7, page 132:

"The word compassion in the original Greek language of the New Testament comes from the word splagna. It literally means 'guts.' Remember from English class the term onomatopoeia—a word that sounds like its meaning? Splagna sounds like your guts, doesn't it? Ever felt something so deeply it hit you in the gut? Maybe you heard tragic news, or someone hurt you deeply, something happened to a child or loved one, and you could feel it down deep inside, couldn't you?

"Do you realize what Matthew 9:36 is saying? Jesus could feel the hurt and heartache, the disease and discouragement, the conflict and confusion of humanity. He felt our pain like a punch in the gut, and his compassion motivated action. He did something about it!"

Discuss:

- When was the last time you felt someone else's pain like a punch in your gut? What happened? What did you do?
- When was the last time you felt that level of compassion for someone who doesn't follow Christ?

 Have someone read aloud this quote from Chapter 7, page 133:

"When Jesus felt moved in his gut by all the distressed, downcast people, do you know what his solution was? To send you! Jesus said in Matthew 9, 'The harvest is plentiful but the workers are few. Ask the Lord of the harvest, therefore, to send out workers into his harvest field' (Matthew 9:37–38). Then he sent them in answer to their own prayer! 'As the Father has sent me, I am sending you' (John 20:21)."

Discuss:

- What if we really did go into the world as "sent ones" doing what Jesus did? What do you think would happen?
- On a scale of 1 to 10 (10 being "totally ready, bring it on!"), how ready do you feel to explain the good news to people God might send you to serve?
- Tell us about a time you had a negative experience trying to share your faith with someone. What happened? What made it negative? If you could do it over, what would you do differently?
- Tell us about a time you had a positive experience sharing your faith with someone. What happened? What made it positive? What did you learn from the experience?
- What are the main differences between our "negative" stories and our "positive" ones?

 Have a few volunteers read aloud the "Summary" boxes in Chapter 8, pages 159, 165, and 168.

Discuss:

- What stands out to you about this example of how to share your faith?
- What aspects of this example would you most like to adopt the next time you share your faith with someone?
- Earlier, you rated your readiness to share your faith on a scale of 1 to 10. What else do you need to do to move your score closer to a 9 or 10?
- Will you? Why or why not?

 Have someone read aloud this quote from Chapter 9, pages 172-173:

"Jesus said the Pharisees were 'technically correct' doctrinally, but missing God's heart: 'Practice and obey whatever they tell you, but don't follow their example' (Matthew 23:3 nlt). Some Christians believe that to accurately represent the gospel message to a fallen world, we must first make sure people understand the 'bad news' that they are sinful and condemned and face judgment; otherwise they won't feel the need to repent and trust the "good news" about Jesus saving them from their sins.

So far, we've seen that Jesus' approach to a broken, sinful world did not start with bad news first, but truly wonderful news first. Without meaning to, this bad-news-first 'gospel' leaves people with a message that says, 'If you accept Christ you are now saved from hell, but still doomed to trying harder, failing, and attempting to live worthy of God's grace on your own power.'

It doesn't lead people to fully trust a loving God to lead them and change them. See the irony? This bad-news-first approach produces a gospel and life of mud management! But there is a time for the 'bad news.'"

Discuss:

- When is it the right time to confront nonbelievers with the "bad news?" How should Christ followers deal with the persistent sin patterns of those who do not follow Christ?
- Do you struggle to speak hard words when they are needed? Why or why not? How might this be the most loving thing you could do for a person?
- What hard words do you think most Christ followers today need to hear?

Have someone read aloud these "hard words" Burke includes for Christ followers at the end of Chapter 9, pages 184-185.

"What's the path to greatness? Our world says greatness comes from moving up. Jesus says, 'You want to be great—good! Move yourself down to serve—better yet, become slave to all! Then you'll be great.'

But we don't really believe Jesus. These are hard words.

We may believe in Jesus, but we don't believe Jesus—we don't trust that he's telling the truth. In fact, most of us don't even consider that he might be telling the truth! That one day, when his kingdom comes fully, those who are greatest for all eternity will be those who held nothing back from serving God by serving others, never ashamed of Jesus or his message.

On [a] trip to Jerusalem, Jesus told [his followers]:

'I assure you that everyone who has given up house or brothers or sisters or mother or father or children or property, for my sake and for the Good News, will receive now in return a hundred times as many houses, brothers, sisters, mothers, children, and property—along with persecution. And in the world to come that person will have eternal life. But many who are the greatest now will be least important then, and those who seem least important now will be the greatest then' (Mark 10:29–31 nlt).

What if Bill Gates said to you, 'Become a servant in my kingdom. That means you must let go of the enjoyments and possessions of your current life; you won't get any recognition or reward; it'll be hard, thankless work; at times it will feel like nobody notices, nobody cares; and people may reject you and look down on you for being my servant. But if you will become the lowest servant in the kingdom of Microsoft for five years, I will make you the greatest in Microsoft. You will be like an adopted heir, sharing all the glory that comes with being greatest in my kingdom.'

Now that we can understand—right? Who in their right mind would not humble themselves and give up everything to become a servant with that kind of promise? You're not giving up anything in reality—you're making a wise choice to gain everything! Jesus promised you something so much greater than that, yet we don't believe it! We don't believe Jesus.

If we did, we would live to serve, and love, and make Jesus known everywhere and with everything: serving people at work, serving our families, serving our neighbors, boldly inviting people into the life Jesus offers, dying to self that worries about the approval of people, dying to greed that spends all our thoughts on getting more rather than giving more.

Here's where Jesus' restoration project often gets delayed even with those who claim to follow him. So I want to challenge you to begin to pray a prayer of surrender: 'God, I open my hands to serve you and others, wherever I am, with all I've got. Make me bold to serve not only their physical needs, but also their spiritual needs as I love them and unashamedly invite them into life with you.'

"With that simple prayer of willingness, God will allow you to share in the greatest work in history, and he gives you back so much more than you ever give."

Discuss:

- Do you agree with Burke's assertion that "we don't believe Jesus" when he says the path to greatness is to become the servant of all? Why or why not?
- What, if anything, is stopping you from voicing the "prayer of surrender" Burke challenges us to pray?

Do 20 MINUTES

As the discussion draws to a close, go around the room and have each person respond to these questions:

- What are you taking away from our time together today? What do you most want to remember from our conversation?
- What action has our discussion inspired you to take in your own life? Will you do it?

Finally, here's a challenge for the entire group to take on together (from the book, page 170):

"Pray for an opportunity to tell someone about the good news, and when the opportunity arises, be bold this week. If you've been doing these exercises with a coworker or neighbor, maybe the ground is fertile to plant this seed."

Ask each person:

- Will you take on that challenge?

We'll check in on how your challenge went the next time we meet. Also, remind everyone to read Chapters 10 through 12 before our next meeting!

Close with prayer, and dismiss.

DISCUSSION GUIDE

Chapters 10 through 12

"Use me, God. Show me how to take who I am, who I want to be, and what I can do, and use it for a purpose greater than myself."
– Dr. Martin Luther King, Jr.

Connect **30 MINUTES**

After everyone has arrived, start the conversation by giving each person a minute or two to "check in" around the following questions:

- How'd it go with your assignment? What happened?
- What did you learn?
- How do you want to apply what you've learned moving forward?

Don't rush through this part. Aside from helping each other "get fully here," checking in on what happened with the previous assignment is a terrific way to learn from one another's challenges and experiences.

NOTE: If you have more than 12 people in your group, form groups of three or four to do your check in.

After everyone has checked in, remind everyone of your shared agreements. Then take a moment to pray, inviting God to open your minds and hearts, to guide your conversation, and to give you courage to follow where He leads.

Discuss 40 MINUTES

Begin by asking:

- What was your reaction to what you read in Chapters 10-12?
- What stood out to you?
- What surprised or intrigued you?
- What did you find confusing or even frustrating?
- What did you learn or discover?

 Have someone read aloud this quote from Chapter 10, pages 196-197:

"The last times Jesus appeared to his followers after the resurrection, he empowered this diverse group of ordinary fishermen, tax collectors, former prostitutes, and 120 others to do extraordinary things by his power! Jesus told them:

'All authority in heaven and on earth has been given to me. Therefore go and make disciples of all nations, baptizing them in the name of the Father and of the Son and of the Holy Spirit, and teaching them to obey everything I have commanded you. And surely I am with you always, to the very end of the age' (Matthew 28:18–20). Don't think for a minute that Jesus expected this group of 120 people to help every nation follow him in their generation. He intended them to equip others who equip others, just like he had modeled. And life by life the torch has now passed to you and your Christian friends.

Have you ever considered that Jesus fully expects you, as his follower, to do the same things he did? Do you realize that you can make disciples (learners and followers of Jesus) by leading them to faith and baptizing them? And do you know that you can teach others, especially those you help lead to faith, to observe all the things Jesus commanded?...Jesus expects to do the same through you. The only question is whether you believe him and will trust him to do in his power what you could never do alone. That won't feel comfortable or easy. It will stretch your faith, but you will experience the adrenaline rush and intimacy with God that only comes by co-laboring with the Lord of the harvest. You don't need to change jobs, go to seminary, or move overseas to the 'mission' field. You just need to look up and see what Jesus sees."

Discuss:

- What's your reaction to this quote?
- What do you think Burke means by saying that "You don't need to change jobs, go to seminary, or move overseas to the 'mission' field. You just need to look up and see what Jesus sees?"
- What is it to practice seeing what Jesus sees in our day-to-day lives?

 Have someone read aloud this quote from Chapter 10, page 202:

"The night before his crucifixion, probably walking toward Gethsemane, Jesus picked up a branch and said, 'Guys, see this branch? A branch doesn't have to stress and strain to bear fruit, it just stays connected to the vine, and fruit grows naturally. I am the vine; you are the branches. If you simply stay connected to me, you will bear much fruit. Apart from me, you can do nothing!' (John 15:5, my paraphrase). Jesus has all authority. He is always with us by his Spirit. As we simply learn to listen to those quiet promptings in our conscience to do his will and participate in his kingdom work, we will bear much fruit. He will produce spiritual vitality within us, and a wave of impact in the world through us."

Discuss:

- When have you heard a prompting from God's Spirit and followed it? What happened?
- What generally stops you from hearing and following God's promptings? Why do you suppose that is?
- What would it take for you to say "yes" to following God's promptings 100 percent of the time (or as close to 100 percent as you can get)?

 Have someone read aloud this quote from Chapter 10, page 200:

"Imagine if you could get a small group to start meeting and praying, 'Lord, send us into your field. Show us the physical and spiritual needs you see. Lead us to be your body doing your work together.' And imagine that nucleus growing as you serve people around you, throw parties and invite those you work with or live near, create 'come as you are' learning spaces where people can explore faith, help others not only follow Christ but discover their gifts and deploy those gifts to function together as a loving body! Imagine small groups forming to help people grow in faith intentionally from finding faith to fully following Christ. Imagine a day when fifty to seventy people feel like one big, extended family, many who came to faith, some still in the process, others who joined as co-missioned Christians, and together you're seeing Jesus change the world around you life by life by life! Feel impossible? 'All things are possible with God' (Mark 10:27)."

Discuss:

- What's your reaction to this vision? What about it excites you the most? What scares you about it?
- What are you afraid might happen if you actually tried this?
- What other concerns do you have about it?
- Bottom line – is it worth it? If not, why not? If so, then what's stopping you from saying yes to getting started this week?

 Have someone read this quote from Chapter 11, pages 213-214:

"It is not enough for one Christian to befriend and share her faith with another person. That worked in a world that was mostly Christian, where most people grew up with a background knowledge of and respect for the Bible, mainly needing the central theme of grace clarified to decide whether to follow Christ. However, in today's post-Christian context, people often need the intersection of three elements in order to find faith and become the church:

1. A friendship with someone who truly acts like Jesus—listening, caring, serving, and talking openly about faith in a non-pressuring way.

2. Relationship with a 'tribe' of four to five other Christians whom they enjoy hanging out with and who make them feel like they truly belong.

3. A 'come as you are' learning environment where they can learn, usually for six to eighteen months, about the Way of Jesus."

Discuss

- What's your reaction to Burke's assertion regarding how people come to faith in Jesus in post-Christian world? Do you agree, disagree, partially agree? Explain.
- Can you see this approach working practically in your own life? Why or why not?

As a group, take a few minutes to brainstorm a list of obstacles that stand in the way of integrating this kind of faith-sharing approach into our lives. Then brainstorm a list of possible creative solutions to the obstacles you listed.

 Have someone read aloud this quote from Chapter 12, page 226:

"To serve or be served? That is the question for those who claim to follow Jesus. Which do we go to church to do? Recall that Jesus said, 'The Son of Man did not come to be served, but to serve, and to give his life as a ransom for many' (Mark 10:45). So what does it mean to follow Jesus? And if God intends his church to function together as Jesus' body (Romans 12:4–8), what would that look like?"

Discuss:

- Read aloud Mark 10:45, and Romans 12:4-8. Based on these verses, what does it mean to follow Jesus together as his body?
- How might you and your friends serve the people God has already put around you – at work, where you live or go to school, or in your relational network?

Do 20 MINUTES

As the discussion draws to a close, go around the room and have each person respond to these questions:

- What are you taking away from our time together today? What do you most want to remember from our conversation?
- What action has our discussion inspired you to take in your own life? Will you do it?

Finally, here's a challenge for the entire group to take on together (from the book, page 235):

"Come up with a serving project with a few other Christians and consider inviting friends who may seem far from God to serve with you." If you have trouble coming up with an idea, consider going through the "heart storming" process together. You'll find it described on page 227.

Ask each person:

- Will you take on that challenge?

We'll check in on how your challenge went the next time we meet. Also, remind everyone to read Chapters 13 through 15 before our next meeting!

Close with prayer, and dismiss.

DISCUSSION GUIDE

Chapters 13 through 15

"Life doesn't happen to us, it happens through us."
– unknown

Connect 30 MINUTES

After everyone has arrived, start the conversation by giving each person a minute or two to "check in" around the following questions:

- How'd it go with your assignment? What happened?
- What did you learn?
- How do you want to apply what you've learned moving forward?

Don't rush through this part. Aside from helping each other "get fully here," checking in on what happened with the previous assignment is a terrific way to learn from one another's challenges and experiences.

NOTE: If you have more than 12 people in your group, form groups of three or four to do your check in.

After everyone has checked in, remind everyone of your shared agreements. Then take a moment to pray, inviting God to open your minds and hearts, to guide your conversation, and to give you courage to follow where He leads.

Discuss 40 MINUTES

Begin by asking:

- What was your reaction to what you read in Chapters 13-15?
- What stood out to you?
- What surprised or intrigued you?
- What did you find confusing or even frustrating?
- What did you learn or discover?

 Have someone read aloud this quote from Chapter 13, pages 240-241:

"Not only does a person from our post-Christian world need to encounter someone with the heart of Jesus and meet several Christians loving and serving like Jesus, they also need time! They need time to learn and understand the way of Christ because they really don't know much more than hearsay. We can't expect people to clean up the mud before learning about God and his restoration process. They need space to come 'as is' and learn without pressure, where it's okay to have doubts, questions, and struggles as they grow in the knowledge of the Lord."

Discuss:

- Have you ever been a part of a "come as you are" church or group, where you could learn without pressure, and openly share your doubts, questions, and struggles without fear of judgment? If so, what was it about that church or group that made it so safe?
- Why do you think churches so often fail to create a genuine "come as you are" environment where people can explore faith without fear?
- What would have to change about most church services or small group gatherings to genuinely make nonbelievers feel welcome there?

 Have someone read this quote from Chapter 15, pages 275-276:

"In the Western church, it is time to rethink what it means to worship and follow Jesus, Lord of the universe, Lord of the harvest. I find too many Christians majoring in the minors: 'Where can I worship (i.e. sing songs) where I really feel drawn into the presence of God?' 'Where can I be fed with teaching that's new and challenging?' 'Where can my kids get the kind of spiritual education that will help them follow God?'

These are good questions in the right context (in the context of being on mission with Jesus). But in the context of just attending church to have your ears tickled with new information, without exercising off the knowledge we've already consumed by engaging a broken world with mercy, it produces a subtle phariseeism.

Worship should not become a weekly 'fix' that gives you an emotional high, yet never translates into a heart that breaks over the things that break the heart of God. If that emotion doesn't motivate you to do something, that's just entertainment with a Christian flavor."

Discuss:

- What's your reaction to Burke's assertion that, when it comes to choosing a church, too many Christians are "majoring in the minors?"
- Has this ever been true of you? Why or why not?
- What are some ways we might reverse this tendency to make church "entertainment with a Christian flavor?"

In Chapter 14, Burke asserts that when it comes to helping others find faith in Christ and grow to maturity, "everyone can develop someone."

Discuss:

- Do you believe this is true? Why or why not?
- Are you currently invested in developing someone spiritually? Why or why not?
- What do you think holds most Christ followers back from intentionally investing in others in this way?

 Have someone read aloud this quote from Chapter 14, pages 265-266:

"The last thing Jesus said to his disciples was 'All authority in heaven and on earth has been given to me. Therefore go and make disciples of all nations, baptizing them in the name of the Father and of the Son and of the Holy Spirit, and teaching them to obey everything I have commanded you. And surely I am with you always, to the very end of the age' (Matthew 28:18–20).

Do you see Jesus' plan to reach the nations? He invested in this one small group of twelve. They couldn't possibly help every nation follow Jesus, so this Great Commission must have been for those they would invest in, and so on, and so on, all the way to you and me.

You can go and lead people to faith, and help them to identify with the Father, Son, and Spirit through baptism. Why? Because all authority was given to Jesus, and he's always with you, and he co-missioned you to do it! And you can teach them to observe all he commanded. You don't have to have a teaching gift or seminary degree because you already have Jesus' authority and his presence to help you do it. Just get into the Scriptures, read them together, and follow his Spirit together in a confessing community! Emphasize living it—not just knowing it—and help others live it out."

Discuss:

- What hesitations or objections come to mind for you when you think about investing in others spiritually the way Burke describes?
- Why do you think the spiritual practice of developing people (taking time to really invest in others) gets neglected so easily?

 Have someone read this quote from Chapter 15, page 283:

"The Jordan River flows into two bodies of water: the Sea of Galilee, where Jesus spent most of his time, and the Dead Sea. I've visited both. In fact, we held baptisms in the Sea of Galilee and floated on the Dead Sea. The Sea of Galilee teems with life. The fresh water causes growth in vegetation all around the area, the fishing industry has always thrived because of the abundance of marine life, and it has provided clean water for humans for millennia.

The Dead Sea has the name for a reason—it's dead! The salt content has so built up over the years that nothing can live in the Dead Sea. With a saline content over eight times saltier than the ocean, the Dead Sea is so dense that floating on it feels like lying on a floatie, without a floatie! The land remains barren around the perimeter. No fish or aquatic life can survive the salty environment—it's completely dead! Yet the two bodies of water are only sixty-five miles apart and the same Jordan River flows into both! The difference—water flows into and out of the Sea of Galilee. In the Dead Sea, water flows in, but no water flows out."

Discuss:

- When have you found yourself thinking about Christian growth as a river flowing into you (to feed you, to encourage you, to have inspiring worship or kids' programs for you), but never flowing back out to bring life to others?
- How might giving to others, building into others, restoring others, grow you into the Masterpiece God intended?
- What else needs to happen in your life for you to make the full transition from a "Dead Sea" lifestyle to a "Sea of Galilee" lifestyle?

At the beginning of our exploration of this book, we each responded to this question, which Burke challenges us to wrestle with throughout the book: "Am I more like Jesus or more like a Pharisee to the people around me?" (page 22). Now that we've come to the end of our exploration, let's each take a moment to share how you'd answer that question now, and what, if anything, has shifted in your understanding of yourself and your impact on those who are far from Christ.

 Once everyone has shared, have someone read aloud Burke's final encouragement to readers from Chapter 15, pages 283-284:

"God sees a Masterpiece in you. He wants to restore you more and more into that work of Art he had in mind all along. Don't ever forget that—he saved you by his grace because you are his Masterpiece, created in Christ Jesus to do the works he prepared for you when you were just an idea in his mind. As you allow him to restore you, that journey will take you into the lives of others who need his restoration work as well. We are restored to restore others. In fact, we can't be restored without allowing the Master Artist to use our lives as tools of restoration in his hands.

"People aren't like paintings or marble sculptures that passively cooperate with the Artist; people have wills of their own. They have hurts, wounds, and secret addictions, and people will disappoint you and hurt you and you will disappoint and hurt them. And yet...in the mess of our human brokenness, God brings beauty. As we cooperate with him, he restores what's been lost, stained, and broken. As you go with the attitude and actions of Jesus, his Spirit will guide you on the adventure of a lifetime. You will see him do things you never thought possible. You'll realize what Jesus meant when he said, 'Nothing is impossible with God' (see Mark 10:27).

All of Jesus' encounters show us this. He entered into the mess with us. He entered into the suffering with us. He entered into deep relationship with us, feeling the disappointment, hurt, and betrayal even to the point of death. Yet in the midst of an imperfect world filled with imperfect people came his greatest work—his Artwork of Grace. And as you learn to worship him with your whole life, living on his mission with Jesus and others, he will clear off the mud and make your life and the lives you encounter into his Masterpiece."

Do **20 MINUTES**

As the discussion draws to a close, go around the room and have each person respond to these questions:

- What are you taking away from our time together today?
- What do you most want to remember from all of our conversations about this book?
- What action has our discussion today inspired you to take in your own life? Will you do it?

Finally, here's a challenge for the entire group to take on together (adapted from the book, page 254):

If your church has a place to bring people exploring faith, invite a few people this week. Do not be discouraged if they don't respond right away; it usually takes multiple invites (like 5–7). If your church doesn't have a place like that, gather a few friends and create one for your church. Follow the model outlined in Chapters 10-15 to make connections, establish community, and start developing people to do life with God and training them to help others to do the same.

Ask each person:

- Will you take on that challenge?

To acknowledge and celebrate this bold step, have each person who takes on the challenge stand up, and invite the rest of the group to gather around them to pray for them and commission them into this new adventure with God!

After the prayer, dismiss the group.

About The Author

John Burke is the author of *No Perfect People Allowed* and *Soul Revolution*, and the lead pastor of Gateway Church in Austin, Texas, which he and his wife founded in 1998. Since then, Gateway has grown to over 4,500 members, made up mostly of unchurched people who began actively following Christ at Gateway. John is also the founder and president of Emerging Leadership Initiative (ELI), a nonprofit organization working to help church planting pastors and ordinary Christians "raise the church out of the culture." John has spoken in 15 countries to over 200,000 church leaders and Christians about reaching a postmodern, post-Christian culture. He and Kathy have been married twenty-three years and currently reside in Austin, Texas, with their two children, Ashley and Justin.

Take The Next Step with *Mud and the Masterpiece*

So what's next?

How can I express the truth in this book through my life?

1. Go to **mudandthemasterpiece.com**, where you will find resources that will help you implement the ideas from the book in your life, church, and small group:

    - Network Action Guide
    - Small Group Discussion Guide
    - Church & Leader Resources

2. Go to **JohnBurkeOnline.com** for ongoing thoughts about living on mission with Jesus and each other.

3. Go to **GatewayLeaders.com** for more leadership training resources from John Burke.

Made in the USA
Lexington, KY
08 June 2014